A Voyage to Outer Space

and Other Cases

Seymour Simon

Illustrations by Kevin O'Malley

Volume **4** in the Einstein Anderson Series

SEYMOUR SCIENCE

An Imprint of StarWalk Kids Media

Published by Seymour Science LLC.

These stories, which have been substantially updated and expanded for a new audience, are based on the Einstein Anderson book originally published in 1980 by Viking Penguin, under the title *"Einstein Anderson Shocks his Friends,"* and republished in 1997 by Morrow Junior Books, New York, under the title *"The Halloween Horror, and Other Cases."*

www.StarWalkKids.com

ISBN: 978-1-936503-18-6 (PRINT)

SEYMOUR SCIENCE
An Imprint of StarWalk Kids Media

Contents

A Voyage to Outer Space

"**Look at that!** It's the space station. We're finally there! Doesn't it look like a giant bicycle wheel?"

"Yes, Commander. But what is that cloud of gas coming out of the wheel? Has the pressure-sized atmosphere been compromised?"

"I think you're right, we had better radio the..."

"Hold on! Cut!" Paloma Fuentes jumped up from her seat in the Sparta Middle School auditorium and walked toward the stage. "Pat, it's not pressure-sized. It's pressurized. It means under pressure. In a space station the atmosphere is kept under pressure to keep it from escaping."

From his spot on the stage, Pat Hong looked at Paloma blankly, then stared at the script in his hand, then back at Paloma. The tall athlete, wearing his Sparta soccer team T-shirt and sweatpants, wasn't used to being in plays. Also, for some reason, he always had trouble talking when Paloma was around.

"Uh, sure Paloma, pressur*ized*," he said, meekly. "Sorry."

"Don't worry about it," Paloma replied, briskly. "Okay, everyone, let's take it from the start of the scene again."

All the actors groaned.

"Come on, Paloma," said Jamal Henry, who was playing the Commander. The thickset kid was wearing the top of his space costume over his green cargo pants. "We've been over this ten times."

"And we're going to keep going over it until we get it right!" Paloma ordered.

"Uh, maybe we need a break," said Einstein Anderson. He was sitting at the "science command center" of the cardboard "space station." Naturally, he was playing the Chief Science Officer.

"Okay, *Einstein*," Paloma agreed, unhappily. "But just five minutes."

Einstein nodded. He was used to Paloma teasing him about his nickname. After all, he was just a normal-looking 12-year-old kid of average height, with light brown hair and a pair of dark-rimmed glasses perched on his nose. With his striped T-shirt and faded jeans, he certainly didn't look like the most famous scientist of the 20th century, the genius who had come up with the famous equation, $E=MC^2$ that unlocked the secret of atomic energy.

Einstein's real name was Adam, but no one called him that anymore, not even his parents. His kindergarten teacher had called him Einstein after he taught her how to make green slime out of cornstarch and water. The nickname stuck because, although Einstein Anderson wasn't a genius, he was always learning about science. Whatever was going on around him, Einstein found ways to use science to answer questions and solve mysteries.

Paloma Fuentes was Einstein's best friend, probably because she was the only other person in Sparta who was as interested in science as he was. They were friends and also friendly rivals, but no matter how hard she tried, Paloma had never been able to beat Einstein with a science mystery.

It was a Paloma who had written the play they were rehearsing, *Escape From Space Station Galileo*. It was the sixth grade entry into the school drama competition, scheduled for just before Thanksgiving. Each grade had to create an original play based on something the students were learning. Naturally, Paloma had volunteered to write a play based on what they had learned about the solar system in science class.

As soon as Paloma announced the break, the actors left the stage, to stretch or get a snack. Some of them took out their phones to text their friends. Meanwhile, Paloma bounced impatiently from one foot to the other, scuffing her red canvas high tops on the floor. She twisted her long, black ponytail in one hand while she looked at the computer tablet in her other.

"Stanley!" she called. "Do you have that special lighting effect ready?"

"Hold your horses!" a voice yelled from the balcony. "I'm working on it."

"That's what you said half an hour ago," Paloma replied.

Einstein hopped off the stage and walked over to Paloma. He looked over her shoulder, and since she was taller than him, he had to stand on tiptoe. Paloma turned around and handed him the tablet.

"I want to project this photo of the rings of Saturn behind the scene," she explained. "Stanley said he would run the lights and projections, but he's being difficult."

"Well, he did want to direct," Einstein reminded her quietly.

"But the class elected me," Paloma replied.

"Yes, but you know Stanley," Einstein said with a smile. "He never forgets."

"Like an elephant," Paloma agreed, then immediately added, with a warning tone, "Einstein…"

It was too late. Einstein was already launching into one of his terrible jokes.

"Hey, why are elephants wrinkled?"

"I don't know, Einstein," Paloma groaned.

"Because they don't fit on ironing boards!"

As usual, Einstein laughed harder at his joke than anyone else.

"Hey, Paloma," Jamal called from the stage. "How about in the weightless scene you rig a harness so I can fly?"

"I don't have a budget for that," Paloma answered. "Besides, I don't think the school will let us do it."

"Just tell them it's for science," he told her, with a big grin. With one hand, he lifted a piece of cardboard scenery that was painted to look like part of a spaceship. "Look, in space everything is like cardboard. There's nothing to it!" he shouted. "I want to fly!"

"Sorry, Jamal," Einstein said, laughing at his friend's antics. "We're doing the play here on Earth. Besides, you don't have the science quite right. Rockets and space stations are the same up in space as they are here on Earth. They don't change just 'cause they go into orbit."

"That's not true," Jamal argued. "Everyone knows stuff in space weighs less. That's the whole point of the next scene."

"Yes," Einstein told him, as he walked to the stage. "Things *weigh* less in space but what they're made of doesn't change. They weigh less because they are farther away from the

Earth and Earth's gravity. They still have the same mass—the same amount of matter. That's the difference between weight and mass. Mass is how much stuff there is and weight is a measurement of how much gravity is pulling on that stuff."

"Uh, okay, Einstein" Jamal said, with a shrug. "If you say so. I just wanted to fly."

"You'll have to get on Broadway to do that," Paloma said. "Okay, everyone, take your places for the space walk scene."

The whole cast quickly assembled and began to read their lines. The scene took place outside the space station. Pat, Jamal, and Einstein pretended to be in space suits with magnetic boots that allowed them to walk on the station without flying off into outer space.

"Commander, where do you want to put this steel beam?" Pat read from the script.

"Help me place it over here," Jamal read, doing his best to sound like a commander. "Science Officer Rodriguez will bolt it to the solar panel tower."

"Okay, Commander," Pat read. Slowly he and Jamal bent over and picked up the large cardboard box that was painted to look like a steel beam. They moved it to the other side of the stage.

"Hold on! Hold on!" shouted a voice from the back of the auditorium. It was Stanley. He came running down the aisle.

"This is all wrong," he said as he came up to the stage.

Stanley was a tall, thin kid with short blond hair. His dream was to be the next big tech billionaire, like Steve Jobs or Bill Gates. He had even made up his own corporation, Stan-Tastic Industries. As president, he always dressed the way he imagined a CEO dressed. Today was no different. Even for a play rehearsal he wore tan chinos, a white shirt and a red and blue striped tie.

"What do you want?" Paloma asked impatiently. "You're interrupting the rehearsal."

"Yes, and a good thing, too," Stanley replied, climbing onto the stage. "Thanks to your lousy direction, we're going to lose the play competition."

"What are you talking about?" Paloma asked, angrily.

"I'm talking about the science mistake in this scene," Stanley replied, sounding confident as always.

"Mistake?" Paloma asked angrily. "What mistake? There's no mistake."

"Sure there is," Stanley told her, as the cast looked on. Some of the kids backstage came out to see what was going on. "And if we send a play to the competition with science mistakes in it, we will lose for sure."

"Okay," Paloma said as she climbed up on the stage also. "If you're so smart, tell us what the mistake is."

"No way," Stanley said, with an evil grin. "It's the director's job to spot these things. Now if I was the director, then it would be my job to spot the mistakes."

"So that's it," Paloma said. "This is just about you trying to become the director."

"No, this is about putting on a play that has good science in it," Stanley replied, looking around. "I'm sure everyone wants that." He fixed his gaze on Einstein. "Isn't that right?"

Einstein just nodded and pushed his glasses back on his nose.

"Come on, Stanley," Jamal said. "Tell us what the mistake is."

Stanley looked awfully pleased with himself. "Well, okay, just to show you that I know what I'm talking about. This scene is supposed to show weightlessness in space. But that's not what Pat and Jamal are doing. They should be able to lift that steel beam easily because it's weightless. In fact, Pat should be able to lift it himself."

"Is that true, Paloma?" Jamal asked.

"Uh, I don't know, let me see," Paloma mumbled. She looked at her computer tablet and quickly swiped through her pages of notes.

"Hah!" Stanley laughed. "A real director would know the answer. I think we should have another vote."

"Hold on," Pat said, though he didn't sound very certain. "Let Paloma have a chance."

"She had her chance," Stanley argued. "I say we vote."

Several of the kids on the stage nodded. Just then Einstein stepped forward.

"Paloma doesn't need another chance," he said quietly. "She got the science right the first time and I can prove it."

Can you solve the mystery? How can Einstein prove that Paloma is right?

"You're Just sticking up for her because she's your friend," Stanley sneered. "Everyone heard you say yourself that things in space are weightless. So the space station crew should be able to move those steel beams easily."

Einstein shook his head. "The problem is, you didn't listen to everything I said, Stanley. Yes, objects in space are weightless, but like I explained to Jamal, they still have mass."

"Yeah?" Stanley blustered. "So what?" He said it loudly, but he didn't sound so sure of himself.

"So," Einstein continued, "if they have mass, that means they still have *inertia*. Inertia is the tendency of objects to resist change in their state of motion. Inertia means that if an object is moving it takes energy to change its direction. And if an object is at rest it takes energy to get it to move."

"But that doesn't make sense," Jamal said. "I don't know what this inertia is, but I think Stanley is right. If something is weightless, you should be able to pick it up without any effort."

Einstein shook his head again. "No, it always takes energy to move something. That's the main thing to remember. You can't move something without applying force and force means energy. If something is weightless in space then it takes less energy to move it than it would if you were on the Earth. That's because you don't have to fight the force of gravity. But it still takes energy. That's why space capsules need rockets and thrusters to move."

Jamal nodded his head, just as Paloma spoke up.

"Here are my notes!" she said, holding up her tablet. "I wrote inertia right here, see?" She held up the tablet so Pat could read it.

"Yeah, that's what it says," he told everyone, sounding proud.

Einstein continued. "So even though the play takes place in space, the actors have to pretend they are putting some effort into moving the steel beams. Even in space, the beams have a lot of mass and it would take energy to move them. And if one person tried to move a big beam like that, once it got moving in a certain direction, physics says it would tend to keep going that way. If there was no one to hold the other end, it might just float off into space! If they were really in space it might even be dangerous. If the beam got out of control it has enough mass to hurt someone. " He turned to Stanley and said with a friendly smile, "Stanley, that's right, isn't it?"

Stanley suddenly looked at his watch. "Hey, I just remembered I have to be somewhere," he said, and he left the stage in a hurry.

"Well Paloma, looks like you're still the director," Einstein said. "So, let's get back to outer space." He paused and a funny look came over his face. "Which reminds me," he said as he began laughing.

"Not another joke," Jamal complained. But Einstein had already started.

"How does the solar system hold up its pants? With an asteroid belt!"

From: Einstein Anderson
To: Science Geeks
Experiment: How to Gain Weight in Space.

Hey, fellow Geeks, here's a riddle for you:

Which weighs more, a pound of rocks or a pound of feathers?

Since you are smart scientists, you probably said they both weigh the same—one pound. But try the riddle on your friends. I bet a lot of them will say the rocks weigh more! It's easy to jump to the wrong answer since rocks are heavier than feathers, but here's another riddle: Which takes up more space, a pound of rocks or a pound of feathers? This time "feathers" is the right answer. That's because it takes a lot more feathers to make a pound. So what's the difference? It's a factor called density. The atoms that make up rocks are much more dense than those in feathers. They are packed together tightly so a small amount, or volume, of rock weighs more than the same volume of feathers.

Since we're on a roll, here's another puzzling question: If you are weightless in space, why don't you disappear?

If something weighs nothing on Earth, it is probably invisible. But if a person goes into space, their size and shape does not change, but their weight does. What's up with that? It's because the *weight* of an object depends upon the force of gravity, but its *mass* does not. Mass is a measure of the number of atoms in an object combined with the density of those atoms. Let's say you weigh 65 pounds (about 30 kilograms) on Earth. If you went to the Moon, where gravity is much less than it is on Earth, you would only weigh 10 pounds (4.5 kilograms). But if you went to Jupiter, which is a very dense planet with stronger gravity than Earth, you would look exactly the same, but you'd weigh 150 pounds (68 kilograms)—as much as a washing machine on Earth! Wherever you were, on Earth, the Moon, or Jupiter, your mass would remain the same; you would still be made of the same number of atoms and the density of those atoms would not change.

So the conclusion is: weight varies, depending upon gravity, but mass stays the same. That's what Stanley and Paloma were arguing about.

What if you were an astronaut who went to live on the International Space Station for several months. How would you live in weightlessness? What could you do to help yourself move about? Maybe you'd like to gain some weight?

Let's try an experiment and see how to gain weight in space.

Here is what you need:

• A bucket
• Strong string or rope
• Water

Do this outside where you can spill water without making a mess!

Double the string and make sure it is strong enough to take a sharp pull without breaking. Tie the string to the handle of the bucket. Use a strong knot. Put some water in the bucket. Turn the bucket upside down. What happens? The force of gravity makes the water pour out onto the ground.

Now, put the same amount of water into the bucket, hold the string firmly and swing the bucket around yourself in a circle. If you start slowly, the bucket will drag along the ground and water may slosh over the sides, but once you get going faster, the bucket will rise up and the water will be forced against the bottom of the bucket, even if the bucket is upside down.

What has happened to the water? Why doesn't it pour out of the bucket?

The Science Solution

Did we make artificial gravity by swinging the bucket? No, but we made another force that acted on the water to push it outward toward the bottom of the bucket and keep it from falling to the ground. We made *centrifugal* force. The mass of the water did not change, but the centrifugal force was acting upon it to push it outward toward the bottom of the bucket. Did you also notice a change in the centrifugal force as the bucket moved faster or more slowly? Right! Centrifugal force is greater when you accelerate the bucket or move it faster.

The reason water doesn't fall out of the bucket is because there is enough centrifugal force to counteract Earth's gravity and keep the water in the bucket. This is very important for space stations and satellites. The closer an object is to the center of the Earth, the stronger the force of gravity. On the surface of Earth, gravity is strong enough to keep solid objects on the ground. As an object like a rocket or space station gets farther away from Earth, the force of gravity gets weaker, but it does not go away completely. A space station in orbit still feels some of the Earth's gravity and it stays in orbit by using rockets to keep moving fast enough that the centrifugal force is exactly enough to counteract Earth's gravity. If there were no centrifugal force, the space station would fall back to Earth.

So if there is gravity in space, why do astronauts feel weightless? Great question! Have you ever been on a roller coaster? Or even on a school bus that goes over a big bump in the road so you bounce up in the air and fall back into your seat? When the roller coaster car goes over the top of the big hill and starts to roll down, or you fly up out of your bus seat, you feel weightless as you begin to fall. Astronauts in space feel weightless because their spacecraft is always falling toward Earth. Centrifugal force keeps the ship from falling back to Earth, and centrifugal force also gives the astronauts enough weight to be able to move around on the ship. So, centrifugal force does help you gain weight in space.

Keep on moving and the force will be with you!

The Terrible Test

It was a Friday afternoon and Einstein's science class was on edge. Their teacher, Ms. Taylor, was returning their latest test and not everyone was happy.

As the teacher went down the rows, handing out the graded papers, Einstein wondered if you could tell whether it was a good or bad grade by the expression on the student's face.

Sometimes, he thought, but not always. For instance, some kids, like Pat Hong, were happy and relieved to just pass. Also, kids who were used to getting As, might look miserable if they got a B.

There was no question about the sort of grade Stanley had gotten. He sat three seats in front of Einstein, and when Ms. Taylor got to him, she stopped.

"Class," she announced, "I want to compliment Stanley for turning in the best test paper in the class. He was the *only* one to get all the answers right." As she handed Stanley his paper he was beaming from ear to ear.

Well, it wasn't that big a surprise that Stanley had gotten a perfect test score, Einstein thought. Stanley could do well when he put his mind to it. But of course, that meant that Einstein *hadn't* gotten a perfect test score, which was odd. Usually he got 100 percent on every science test. He figured he must have made a careless mistake.

Ms. Taylor stopped next to Einstein's desk. She looked very disappointed as she handed him his test paper.

"I'm very surprised at *you*, Adam," she said, shaking her head slowly. She was one of the few teachers who never used Einstein's nickname. "This is not like you at all."

From his seat near the front of the class, Stanley turned around and gave Einstein an evil grin.

Einstein took the piece of paper. It was not hard to see why Ms. Taylor was surprised. Written in red pencil at the top was the mark C-minus. Einstein was surprised, too. He couldn't remember the last time he'd gotten less than an A on a science test. He stared at the paper. It seemed like almost half of his answers were marked wrong. He couldn't have made that many careless mistakes, could he?

He read the very first question:

"Plants turn toward sunlight because of a property called: a) photographic memory, b) photon torpedoes, c) photogenic movement d) phototropism."

Einstein knew the correct answer was d, phototropism, but somehow he had circled answer b, photon torpedoes. What was he thinking? Photon torpedoes weren't even real—they were from Star Trek.

Feeling a little bit in shock, Einstein looked over the rest of the test paper. It was filled with silly mistakes like that. He was so absorbed that he didn't even hear Ms. Taylor tell the class to break up into their lab teams.

"Hey, *Einstein*," said a friendly voice. "What

happened? Did you have a brain malfunction?"

It was Paloma. She was in the class, too, and of course, she was Einstein's lab partner. She was standing next to his seat with her test paper in her hand. Einstein could see a big red A on her paper.

"I don't know," Einstein told her. "I remember thinking I got all the answers right. But this is a mess."

He held up his test.

"Let me see that," Paloma said, and took the paper out of his hand. She held it up to the light and squinted. "Einstein," she said, "look at all these erasures. Did you really change your mind about every answer?"

Einstein took the paper back and held it up to the light the way Paloma had. He could clearly see that many of his answers had been changed.

"I didn't change any answers," he said. "I'm sure of it."

"Then there's only one possibility," Palomar replied, a little dramatically. "Between the time we took the test yesterday and the time Ms. Taylor marked them, someone else changed your answers. And I think I know who!" She looked straight at Stanley, who was across the room talking to his lab partner.

"Well, I wouldn't be surprised," Einstein said. "But we have no proof."

"Then let's get some," Paloma told him.

Einstein nodded and with his test paper in hand, got up and went to the front of the room, where Ms. Taylor was sitting at her desk. Paloma followed.

"Ms. Taylor," he said, quietly, so no one else could hear. "There's something wrong with this paper."

Ms. Taylor nodded kindly. "I know, Adam," she said. "But don't worry. Everyone has an off day now and then. I'm sure you'll do better next time."

"That's just it," Einstein said. "I know I did better *this* time. I didn't erase all these answers." He held the paper up so the teacher could see the places where his answers had been changed.

Ms. Taylor frowned, then shook her head. "Einstein, are you sure you didn't erase them? I hope you're not just trying to get a better grade."

"But just look," Einstein told her. "The only answers that were changed were changed from correct to incorrect. There's no way I did that."

The teacher looked at the paper carefully, then slowly nodded.

"I have to admit, it doesn't seem like you," she said, finally. "But what are you saying? That someone else changed your answers?"

Paloma interrupted. "Ms. Taylor, where do you keep the test papers?"

"In a file cabinet in the storage room next door," she replied. "But the room is locked and the file cabinet is locked, too."

"Could we take a look?" Paloma asked.

The teacher looked doubtful, then smiled. "Well, I've heard about Adam's mystery solving abilities. But I never knew that you were his Dr. Watson," she said to Paloma. "Okay, let's see you at work."

She got up, went to the door to the storage room, and unlocked it. Then she led Einstein and Paloma inside. On one wall was a poster of the periodic table of elements. Opposite that was a large metal storage locker and a row of tall file cabinets. The room was bright and sunny thanks to a large window at the far end.

A plant sat on top of the cabinets. It was growing in a brown pot and its broad, green leaves were leaning toward the doorway.

Einstein looked around without touching anything. It was clear he was studying the room. Paloma spoke up.

"Ms. Taylor," she asked. "You said this room is kept locked. Did anyone besides you go in here since the test yesterday?"

"Hmm, I don't think so," Ms. Taylor replied. "No, wait! Stanley needed some chalk and I unlocked it for him yesterday."

Paloma fidgeted with excitement. "And what about the key to the file cabinet?" she asked.

"Oh, I keep that in my bag," Ms. Taylor answered. Then she added, "Although there is a spare key here." She stepped to the file cabinet and lifted up the plant. "Here it is. But I never use it."

"And has anyone besides you and Stanley been in here since then?" Einstein asked.

Ms. Taylor shook her head. "No," she said, "but you don't really think Stanley would ruin your test, do you? He's such a nice boy."

"Ms. Taylor, are you sure that you didn't use the spare key yesterday to open the file cabinet?" Einstein asked. "You didn't touch the plant?"

"I'm sure," she nodded. "I'm going to ask Stanley in here right now. I can't believe he would do something so terrible."

Ms. Taylor stepped to the doorway and called to Stanley in the classroom. A moment later he entered the storeroom.

"Stanley," Ms. Taylor said gently. "Now don't get upset, but when you were in here yesterday, getting chalk, did you open the file cabinet?"

Stanley looked shocked. "No, Ms. Taylor," he said innocently. "Why would I do that?"

"Don't lie!" Paloma cried. "You know you opened the file cabinet and changed Einstein's test!"

"Paloma!" Ms. Taylor scolded. "That's a terrible thing to say. You have no proof."

"Ms. Taylor," Stanley said sweetly. "I don't know what she's talking about. Besides, isn't the file cabinet locked?"

"Yes, it is," Ms. Taylor nodded.

Stanley looked like he was going to cry. "Well just because Einstein is upset about his test grade, that's no reason to be accusing me of stuff," he said.

"And you never lifted the plant to get the spare key?" Paloma asked, still angry.

"No, I did not," Stanley stated calmly.

"Well, someone moved it, and you're the only person who came in here besides Ms. Taylor," Einstein said.

"You're nuts!" Stanley said. "How do you know I moved the plant? Prove it!"

"That's exactly what I'm going to do," Einstein replied.

Can you solve the mystery? How can Einstein prove that Stanley moved the plant?

"**The proof** is right here," Einstein said, holding up his test paper.

"Just cause you got a C minus, that's no proof I changed your answers!" Stanley sneered.

"No," Einstein replied coolly. "I mean the proof is in the first question. That is, if you know the correct answer. Plants turn toward sunlight because of a property called: d) phototropism."

"Yeah, so what?" Stanly said, but he seemed suddenly very nervous.

"So, this plant's leaves are leaning *away* from the window!" Paloma cried. "That means they used to be pointing toward the window until someone moved them very recently. Like you did, yesterday!"

"Stanley!" Ms. Taylor said, sounding very shocked. "Did you really do it? Did you really take the key and change Adam's test answers?"

"I...I..." Stanley spluttered and looked around for a way out. "I can't remember," he said finally.

"Well, you'd better come with me," Ms. Taylor said. "We'll see if your memory gets better when you talk to the principal. And Adam, I'll let you take a make up test, if that's all right."

"Sure, Ms. Taylor," Einstein replied. "That would be great."

"Well, we did it," Paloma said as they went back to the classroom. "We solved another mystery."

"Oh, it wasn't so hard," Einstein replied, with a funny grin on his face.

"Oh, don't say it!" Paloma protested. But it was too late.

"After all," Einstein continued, laughing, "Stanley *planted* the evidence!"

From: Einstein Anderson

To: Science Geeks

Experiment: Light at the End of the Tunnel

Hello fellow Geeks!

Nobody ever claimed that plants could talk, but Ms. Taylor's plant told me all I needed to know to expose Stanley's plan to get me a bad grade on the science test.

Thinking about *phototropism*, the way plants respond to light by growing toward it, made me wonder. Do animals respond to light too? Let's do an experiment with some earthworms and find out!

Here is what you need:

- A plastic shoe-size box with a lid where you can cut a hole
- Black construction paper
- Tape
- Flashlight
- Moist paper towels

- Red cellophane (optional)
- Cooking timer
- 4–6 worms

You can buy worms from a bait store or scientific supply house, or even garden catalogs, but it's fun to find your own. Earthworms are called "night crawlers" because they come out in the evening, especially when it has been raining. Worms have to come out of the soil when it rains hard or else they will drown. At night and during dark, cloudy days, worms come out and feed on grass, leaves, and bits of plants. Often they drag their food back into their burrows. Worms are found throughout the United States, Europe, and Eastern Asia, except in desert areas or mountains where the ground stays frozen for most of the year.

Walk softly when you are hunting for worms. A heavy step will make them quickly disappear under ground.

You can also dig for worms. Dig your shovel about 10 inches (25 centimeteres) into the ground, lift up the soil, and put it on a piece of newspaper. Then go through the soil gently with your hands so that you don't hurt the worms.

When you bring your worms home or to school, keep them in a wide-mouth jar or aquarium with moist soil mixed with sand and give them leaves, grasses, or fruit or vegetable peelings for food. Worms must stay moist, but not soaking wet, or they will die.

Now for the experiment. First, we have to prepare our experimental chamber. Take the lid off the box and make a barrier or fence across the middle of the box with black construction paper. Leave a gap of about ¼ inch (about 0.5 centimeters) at the bottom of your barrier so that worms can crawl under it to go to one side or the other and tape the barrier to the lid.

Cover the inside of one side of the lid up to the barrier with black construction paper so no light gets in on that side. Cut a hole on the other side of the top, big enough for a flashlight, about 2 inches (5 centimeters) in diameter.

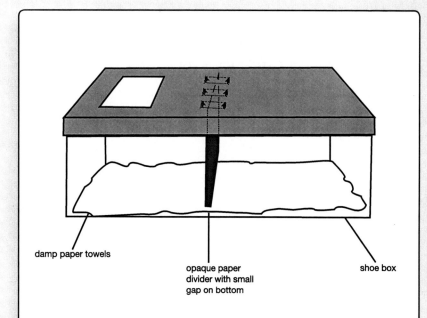

damp paper towels

opaque paper
divider with small
gap on bottom

shoe box

Put moist paper towels on the bottom of the box.
Place two worms in the center of the box and then put
on the lid. Turn on your flashlight and set it on top of
the box, over the hole. Wait five minutes and then take
off the top. Did your worms move? Where did they go
—to the light side of the box or the dark side of the
box?

Record what these two worms did and then try again
with two more worms. When you have tested all your
worms, make a chart showing how many worms went

to the light side and how many went to the dark side. For fun, you can have a race with a friend. See whose worms go to the dark side faster. For an interesting variation, try putting red cellophane over the flashlight. Does coloring the light change the worms' behavior?

The Science Solution

The reaction of plants to light is called phototropism. The reaction of animals to light is called phototaxis. Some animals such as moths and many other insects are attracted to light, while others, such as earthworms, move away from light. Think about what you know about earthworms and where they live. Their habitat is underground. They also have a lot of predators such as birds, snakes, and other animals. Can you think why worms would want to get away from light?

Another strange fact is that earthworms are very simple animals. They don't have eyes, ears, or even lungs! They have sensory cells that allow them to perceive only a few things. There are light-sensing cells on worms' head-end so they can get to the light when they need to escape too much rain underground, and though they can't hear, they are able to sense heavy footsteps and run away. But how do they breathe without out lungs?

Maybe you've noticed that worms look shiny, almost slimy. In fact, their bodies are covered with a layer of mucus which keeps them moist and allows them to take in oxygen from the soil. The oxygen dissolves in the mucus and the worm "breathes" through its skin.

That may seem strange, but worms are an incredible success story. According to the University of Georgia, if you could weigh all the animal life in the world, half of the weight would be worms!

The Shiny Pennies

It was a Saturday morning in early December, but it was so warm, it seemed like a day in spring. The sun was shining, and an overwintering blue jay made a racket in a nearby tree.

"Einstein, why don't you take Dennis and go to the park this morning?" Emily Anderson said, from her place by the kitchen table.

Einstein paused in mid-stride as he was about to go out the back door. He had on his light blue jacket and his favorite pair of ripped jeans.

"Aw, come on," he said. "I told you I was going over to Pat's house. He was going to help me practice my soccer dribble."

"I have a story to finish up." His mom was an editor and reporter at the *Sparta Tribune* and she often brought work home on her laptop. "And if Dennis is around the house I'll never get anything done."

Dennis was Einstein's eight-year-old brother.

"Why don't you take him along to Pat's?" his mom said cheerfully. "I'm sure Pat won't mind."

Dennis chose that moment to come into the kitchen.

"Won't mind what?" he asked. He was still in his pajamas, and his brown hair was falling over his freckled face.

"Won't mind going with Einstein to Pat's house," Emily Anderson replied.

"Pat?" Dennis repeated. "I like Pat."

"You do?" Einstein asked, sounding surprised.

"Yeah," Dennis answered. "He doesn't talk about science all the time, not like Paloma. Or you." Dennis stuck his tongue out at his brother.

"Well, that's nice, dear," their mother said absently as she read her story on the computer screen.

"But I need help with my penny collection!" Dennis said. With that, he lifted a plastic bag full of pennies and dumped them out on the kitchen table with a loud crash. The coins scattered across the white tabletop. Some were bright copper color and others were dull brown. A few were tinted with a bluish green color. Mrs. Anderson looked up, surprised.

"Was that necessary, Dennis?" she asked sternly.

"I guess not," he admitted. "I've been collecting pennies all week, now I need someone to help me research what I have. There's a web site that tells you what old coins are worth. Some of these pennies might be worth millions! Where's Dad?"

Matt Anderson, Einstein's dad, was a veterinarian. "He went out to the Jones farm again," Mrs. Anderson said. "He won't be back till after lunch." She turned to Einstein. "Can't you *please* take Dennis with you?"

"Oh, sure," Einstein replied. He looked at his brother. "I was going to ride my bike over to Pat's. You'd better get dressed."

"Great!" Dennis shouted and ran for the front stairs. "Pack up my coin collection, will you?"

Einstein groaned but he began to shove the loose coins into the plastic bag.

After Dennis got dressed, the two brothers got on their bikes and rode to Pat's house. Dennis tied his plastic bag full of coins to his handlebars.

As they rode, Einstein tried to point things out to Dennis. He stopped and picked up a blue jay feather that was on the ground.

"Feel how light the feather is," Einstein said, handing it to Dennis. "A feather is light, strong, and a good insulator besides. Birds are warm-blooded you know. Feathers help keep their body heat from escaping."

"That's nuts, *Einstein*," Dennis said, teasing him about his nickname. "Everyone knows feathers help birds to fly."

Einstein shrugged. He had a feeling that Dennis sometimes argued just to annoy him. So he switched the subject.

"You know, some of those pennies of yours are pretty *oxidized*," he said.

"Oxy what?" Dennis asked.

"Oxidized. Tarnished," Einstein explained. "The surfaces of coins, especially copper coins, react with chemicals in the air or on people's hands. A thin layer of the metal changes chemically. On a silver coin, tarnish looks dull gray or black. On an old penny, it looks green or dark brown."

"I thought that old pennies were just made that way," Dennis said, sounding interested for once. "How can I clean them off?"

"Well, you can clean pennies lots of ways," Einstein replied. "With soap and water, or vinegar or even olive oil. But collectors say *not* to clean old coins. Cleaning them makes them less valuable."

"Oh, now you're being nuts again, Einstein," Dennis said. "How can a dirty penny be worth more than a clean one?"

"Because if you clean off the tarnish, you take off some of the surface of the coin," Einstein explained. "That makes it less valuable to a collector."

"Wait till I tell mom that dirt is valuable," Dennis said with glee.

They got on their bikes and began to ride again.

"Which reminds me," Einstein said with a silly grin, as they glided down the street. "Why can you always find a lost penny?"

"Oh, not another stupid..." Dennis began, but Einstein interrupted him.

"Because of the scent!" he laughed.

Just then they turned the corner and Dennis's bike hit a pothole. The bike leapt a foot into the air and Dennis landed hard. Einstein braked his bike, jumped off, and rushed to his brother, but Dennis was fine.

His bike had fallen over but he was still standing.

"Are you okay?" Einstein asked.

"No!" Dennis wailed. "My pennies! Look!"

The plastic bag had split open and Dennis's penny collection had scattered all over the street.

"Come on, I'll help you pick them up," Einstein said. "Just be careful of cars."

"I'll help, too!"

The brothers looked up to see Stanley Roberts running toward them on the sidewalk.

"Don't worry, I'll find your pennies," he cried and before Einstein or Dennis could say a thing, Stanley was on his hands and knees in the street picking up pennies and stuffing them in his coat pockets.

"Hey!" Dennis yelled. "Those are my pennies."

"I know, Stanley replied. "Relax. I'm just collecting them for you."

Dennis didn't seem very sure, but he was too worried to stop picking up pennies and argue. It only took a minute for him and Einstein and Stanley to pick up every last cent.

"Here," Einstein said, handing Dennis a handful of coins. "That bag is shot. Keep them in your pocket."

Dennis did as Einstein suggested, then turned to Stanley.

"Good thing I was walking by," Stanley said. "Here you go," he said, dropping a handful of pennies into Dennis's hand.

"Uh, thanks," Dennis said.

"I didn't know you collected pennies"Stanley replied.

"I just started," Dennis told him.

"Well, I'm an expert on old coins," Stanley

said, proudly. "And maybe I can help you with your collection."

"Help me?" Dennis asked. "How?"

"I can help you sell them. For a small commission, of course.'

"Come-Ish-On?" Dennis said, repeating the word slowly. "What's that?"

"Oh, you give me ten percent of whatever you get for the coins," Stanley replied, matter-of-factly. It's worth it because I'll make sure you get the most money for them."

Dennis looked at Einstein, who said, "I don't know if you really need someone to help you sell them. We can look them up on the Internet, like you planned."

"Oh, your brother always thinks he knows more than anyone else," Stanley said, quickly. "But this time he's wrong. Now the first thing we do is clean these coins up."

"Huh?" Dennis answered. "Real collectors don't clean their coins. It makes them worth less! Right, Einstein?"

Einstein nodded.

"Not the way I do it," Stanley replied. "Stan-Tastic Industries has a method for taking tarnish off of coins without removing any of the metal. It will make these pennies super shiny so collectors will want to buy them!"

"Really?" Dennis said.

"Sure," Stanley replied. "That will make them worth even more."

"Uh, I don't think so, Stanley," Einstein said. "Your method for cleaning coins isn't possible and I can prove it."

Can you solve the mystery? How can Einstein prove that Stanley's coin cleaning method won't work?

"**Stanley,**" Einstein asked. "You can't remove the tarnish without removing some of the metal."

"Oh, no, *Einstein?*" Stanley sneered. "Says who?"

"Says the laws of science," Einstein explained calmly. "Tarnish is formed from the top layer of metal. In fact you could say it *is* the top layer of metal that has gone through a chemical change. You can't remove the tarnish without removing a thin layer of the coin. That's why collectors don't do it. Cleaning off the tarnish removes some faint marks made when the coin was minted."

"What do you say to that?" Dennis asked.

Stanley suddenly took out his phone and stared at it for a second. "Oh, you know what?" he said suddenly. "I just realized I have to be someplace. Gotta go, sorry!"

"Gee, thanks, Einstein," Dennis said as they watched Stanley hurry down the block. "As usual, Stanley didn't know what he was talking about."

"That's okay," Einstein said. He took out his cell phone. "I think your bike is broken. I'm going to call mom and have her pick us up. Hey, that reminds me!"

Dennis frowned, and started to object, but then he said, "Oh, go ahead."

"What do you get when you cross a bicycle with a flower?" Einstein asked, giggling. Without waiting, he said, "Bicycle petals!"

From: Einstein Anderson
To: Science Geeks
Experiment: Penny Magic

Stanley tried hard to get his hands on my brother's penny collection. But if he had scrubbed those pennies to get them clean he would have taken off part of the penny in the process.

Have you ever wondered what the Statue of Liberty is made of and why she is green? The short answer is her outer shell is made of copper and the colorful coating is called "verdigris." Here is an experiment with pennies where you will be able to see how copper turns green, how to get it copper-colored again, and how to make steel nails look as if they are made of copper. It's all done with the magic of chemistry.

Here is what you need:

• 20 or more dull pennies
• ¼ cup white vinegar
• 1 teaspoon salt
• A shallow glass or plastic bowl (not metal)

- 2 clean steel nails
- 1 steel screw or bolt
- Paper towels
- Water
- A pen

Take ¼ cup of white vinegar and put it into the bowl with a teaspoon of salt. Stir until the salt dissolves in the vinegar. Take a penny and hold it halfway submerged in the salt and vinegar for 30 seconds. Remove the penny from the liquid. What happened?

Dump the rest of the pennies into the salt and vinegar solution. You will see changes happening for a few seconds and then it will seem as if nothing is happening, but leave the pennies in the solution for 5 minutes.

Take half of the pennies out of the solution and put them on a paper towel to dry. Take the other half of the pennies and rinse them well in water. Put them on another paper towel and use your pen to write "rinsed" on the towel. **Do not throw away the solution you used to clean the pennies!!!**

Leave the pennies alone for an hour or so. In the meantime, put the two nails into the bowl with the used solution, one half in and half out and the other all the way submerged. Add the steel screw and watch what happens. Do you see bubbles coming from the screw? Is there a difference between the nail that is submerged and the one that is half-in and half-out? What is going on here?

The Science Solution

Chemistry!

First, let's go back to those pennies you put in the salt and vinegar solution. When you dipped the penny into the solution, the part that was submerged looked clean and coppery and the other half stayed the color it was before. When you dumped all the pennies in, they also went back to shiny and new. But have a look at them now. Is there a difference, now, between the ones you rinsed and the ones you did not rinse? What is going on?

New pennies are a shiny, reddish color, but over time the copper in the pennies bonds with oxygen or sulfur in the air to make copper oxide or copper sulfide. When you place the pennies in the salt and vinegar solution, the acetic acid from the vinegar dissolves the copper oxide, leaving behind shiny clean pennies. You can't see it, but some atoms of copper from the copper oxide stay in the liquid. When you rinse the clean pennies, the water stops the chemical reaction and the pennies stay clean, but when they are not rinsed, the salt and vinegar left on the pennies encourages oxygen in the air to bond with the copper in the coins and it makes a green coat of *verdigris*, just like the Statue of Liberty.

So, what happened to the nails and the bolt in the leftover salt and vinegar solution? The copper atoms from the pennies that stayed in the solution left some of their electrons on the pennies. Now they are not atoms of pure copper metal, which are neutral, but positively charged copper ions, which are looking for negatively charged particles to bond with. When you add steel nails, the salt/vinegar solution dissolves some of the iron and iron oxides on the surface of the nail, leaving a negative charge on the surface of the nail. Opposite charges attract, so the copper ions are attracted to the nail and a copper coating forms on the nail.

Did you also notice some bubbles rising from the threads in the screw? This is hydrogen gas, which is released in a reaction between hydrogen ions from the vinegar and the metal.

So now you know how to make pennies green—and how to clean them up! I don't think we want to try to take the verdigris off the Statue of Liberty, though, do you? Verdigris protects copper from further oxidation. People once talked about painting the Statue of Liberty, but decided against it because verdigris is the best way of preventing any damage from oxidation. Iron will rust, or *oxidize*, all the way through and rusted iron will eventually break, but verdigris is very strong and it protects copper objects from breaking. That's why people make roofs out of copper in very cold, damp places like Scandinavia.

The Disappearing Snow Statues

One day in early January, every kid at the Sparta Middle School hurried to get to school. The first big snowfall of the year had taken place the day before and everyone knew what that meant— the Sparta Middle School snow sculpture contest. Each grade was allowed one entry in the contest and the class teams had already been picked.

Naturally, Paloma had volunteered to be captain of the sixth grade snow sculpture team. Everyone (except Stanley) was very happy with the way she had directed the sixth grade entry in the play contest. And that was in spite of the fact that they had come in second. Most kids agreed the eighth graders had cheated by putting on a musical.

The snow sculpture contest started in the afternoon. The first step was to pile up as much snow as possible and plan the sculpture. Then the carvers got to work until three o'clock. The contest finished the next morning, when the judging took place. A committee of parents and teachers would award prizes to the biggest and to the most creative snow sculpture.

Einstein, Pat and Jamal were all on the snow sculpture team. So was Stanley, who for once didn't seem to want to make trouble. By mid afternoon, they had all shoveled and hauled enough snow to make a huge pile on their side of the schoolyard. When they took a break to look at their work, Einstein got his book bag and took out a large thermos. He unscrewed the top and held up some paper hot cups.

"Who wants some hot chocolate?" he asked. "My mom knew we'd be working outside today."

He poured some into cups and handed them out. He even gave one to Stanley.

"This is good," Jamal said, smacking his lips. "And still warm."

"This thermos has good insulation," Einstein nodded.

"Not as good as the one I'm inventing for StanTastic Industries," Stanley said, sipping from his cup. "My thermos won't allow any cold to get in."

Einstein looked at Paloma. He knew he should probably stay quiet, but he couldn't help himself.

"Uh, you mean, the insulation won't let any *heat out*, right, Stanley?" he said, quietly. "You know, because that's what insulation does, it keeps *heat* from transferring between objects."

"Oh, yeah," Stanley said, without missing a beat. "That's what I meant. My insulation doesn't let any heat, uh, transfer between objects."

"Can you invent a thermos that's always full of this hot chocolate?" Jamal asked. "Because I'd definitely buy *that*."

"I'm working on that right now," Stanley joked and they all laughed.

"You know this sculpture reminds me of something," Einstein said.

"No, don't!" Pat shouted. But it was too late.

Einstein was already laughing. "Do you know what falls but never gets hurt?"

"No, what?" Paloma grumbled.

"Snow," Einstein giggled.

Paloma frowned and shook her head. "Okay, it's time for step two," she said, holding up her tablet. "Here's what the design should look like." On the screen was a line drawing of the design for the sculpture. It was a panther, the school mascot.

"My aunt helped me make a 3-D rendering of it," she added. She tapped the screen and the view of the sculpture shifted, so you could see it from every angle.

Stanley turned out to have a talent for carving snow, so Paloma put him in charge of shaping the design. He enjoyed telling the other kids which parts of the pile to build up and which parts to carve away. He wasn't too bossy, so

they followed his orders without too much complaint. Soon it was almost three o'clock and the pile had begun to take the rough shape of a panther, getting ready to leap.

"That's really good," Pat said, standing back. "Anyone see what the eighth grade is doing?"

"They're making a polar bear," Jamal replied. "Our panther is way better."

"And the seventh grade is making a castle," Stanley added. "Not very original. I bet we win."

"Maybe," Einstein said, looking at the sky. "But I think we have a problem."

Paloma followed his gaze. Einstein was looking at the sun. Even though it was low in the sky, it was still shining pretty brightly, bright enough to melt the snow. Small pools of water had formed at the base of their panther.

Paloma took out her tablet and tapped the

screen. "Uh-oh," she said as the group gathered around her. "Look at the weather report. The temperature is going up. It won't even be below freezing tonight."

"What are we going to do?" Jamal asked.

"I don't know," Paloma replied. "We have to keep the snow from melting. Anyone have any ideas?"

Everyone fell silent. Einstein pushed his glasses back on his nose and thought hard.

"What we need is a giant ice cooler," Pat murmured.

"Pat, what did you say?" Paloma asked. The big athlete turned red in the face.

"I . . . I . . ." he stuttered.

"He said we need a giant cooler," Stanley said. He shook his head. "I'm building one at StanTastic Industries, but it's not finished yet. Too bad."

"That is too bad," Einstein told them. "But Pat's idea is the right one. Except instead of a giant cooler, we need blankets."

"Blankets?" Stanley objected. "That's nuts! Everyone knows you use blankets to keep things warm. If you put blankets on the sculpture, it will melt faster! You've lost it, Einstein."

"No, blankets are exactly what we need," Einstein replied. "And I can prove it."

Can you solve the mystery? How can blankets keep the sculpture from melting?

"It's true, blankets keep you warm," Einstein explained. "But that's because they are insulators. They keep heat from transferring from your body to the air. But like all insulators, blankets keep heat from moving in either direction. So they will keep the heat from the air away from the snow sculpture." He paused and then added. "Isn't that right, Stanley?"

"Uh, yeah, that's right!" Stanley declared. "That's what I meant to say. I mean, that's what I said."

"Really, cause it sounded like you were saying the opposite," Paloma muttered, but Stanley just ignored her.

Pat and Jamal didn't look very convinced, so Einstein continued.

"I got the idea from Pat," he told them.

"You did?" Pat said, sounding surprised.

"Sure, your idea about the giant cooler. It's the same principle. A cooler can keep things hot or cold. Insulation can keep heat in or it can keep heat out. That's why we can use blankets to keep heat from getting to our snow sculpture."

"Where can we get blankets?" Jamal asked.

"We'll ask Ms. Taylor," Paloma said.

"But don't tell the other classes!" Stanley whispered. "That way, tomorrow we'll be the only ones with a sculpture."

"No, we're going to tell everyone," Einstein replied. "That way we'll win fair and square."

"Ah, I guess," Stanley said, sounding disappointed.

"With any luck it won't get any warmer," Paloma said, looking at her tablet. "Even with the blankets, a little cold weather would really help."

"Hey, that reminds me," Einstein said with a laugh.

"Oh, no," Paloma groaned. "What now?"

"Where do penguins go to see a movie?" he said between giggles. "A dive-in!"

Thanks to Einstein's idea about using blankets as insulators, the sixth grade snow sculpture survived the night. And the next day, the judges declared the sixth grade panther the winning snow sculpture.

From: Einstein Anderson
To: Science Geeks
Experiment: Hot or Not? (THESE EXPERIMENTS MIGHT BE DANGEROUS. BE SURE TO HAVE AN ADULT HELP YOU IF YOU TRY TO DO THEM.)

Hey, Geeks, we won! Don't you just love it when science makes you do something that seems completely impossible—and it works? Who would imagine that the way to keep a snow sculpture from melting is to put a blanket over it? But we used the principle of insulation to keep the heat from the air away from our sculpture. Here's an interesting thought: You can measure heat with a thermometer, but can you measure cold? Heat is a kind of energy but cold is not energy, it is just less heat!

Want to find out more about what heat is and how it travels? Let's do some experiments and see.

CAUTION: You will need adult help because these experiments require matches or a stove.

Here is what you need:

• Some pennies
• A metal saucepan
• A hot plate or stove
• Matches
• 2 balloons
• Water
• A large cup or small bowl
• 3–4 spoons made from different materials—wood, metal, plastic or china

First of all, what is heat? Have you ever seen a pot of water boiling on the stove? What is that vapor that comes out of the pot? Why isn't it there before the water begins to boil?

Here's a demonstration to give you an idea. Pile some pennies on top of each other and then use another penny as a "shooter" to toss into the pile. What happens when the shooter knocks down the pile of pennies? The answer is that the energy from the penny you threw transferred to the pennies in the pile and they moved.

Heat is also a form of energy. We get a lot of our heat energy from the sun, but we also burn fuels like wood, oil, and gas to make heat. When you put a pot of water on the stove and turn on the heat, the heat energy transfers from the stove to the pot to the water inside the pot. As the water gets hotter, its atoms begin to move faster and faster. Finally, when the water gets very hot it changes from liquid water to a gas called water vapor or steam, which rises up into the air. If you put an object such as a pan into a cloud of steam, it would feel hot. (DANGER: DON'T TRY THIS WITHOUT AN ADULT HELPING YOU.) The heat energy from the steam would flow from the steam into the pan. The pan would also get wet because as the heat flows from the steam to the pan, the steam cools and the vapor turns back into liquid water.

Now take a pan or a pot and fill it with hot water from the sink. Put the pot on the counter. Using your thermometer, measure the temperature of the water. Leave it for five minutes. Measure the temperature again. What happened to the heat in the water? Feel the counter under the pot carefully. Some of the heat in the water transferred to the counter and some went into the air. Heat always travels from hotter places and surfaces to cooler ones.

So, here's an experiment: Ask an adult to help you. Blow up a balloon and hold it over a lit candle. What happens? The heat thins the rubber and the balloon pops! Now, fill a balloon halfway with water and then blow it up the rest of the way. Ask your adult helper to hold this balloon over the candle. What happens now? The balloon did not pop because the heat transferred from the candle to the water inside the balloon, which absorbed it.

Now put some very hot water into a cup or bowl and put the spoons in without touching each other. Wait a few seconds and touch the spoons one by one. What do you notice?

The Science Solution

All the animals, plants , minerals, and things around you—including yourself—are made of matter. Matter comes in three forms, solid, liquid, and gas. The pot and spoons and balloons are all solids, water and melted candle wax are liquids and air and steam are gasses. All matter has weight and it takes up space. But there are some things around us that are not matter. Heat and electricity are not matter, they are energy. Energy is the ability to do work. Light makes plants grow. Heat changes batter into a cake. Electricity makes a light bulb glow. Energy has no weight and it does not take up space, but it does do work. Everything around you is either matter or energy.

As we saw in our demonstration with the pennies, energy can be transferred from one object to another. When heat energy travels it makes atoms move faster and bump against each other, which can change the chemistry of something (like turning batter into cake) or change its state from solid to liquid or from liquid to gas.

Some materials conduct heat better than others. You saw this in the activity with the spoons. The metal spoon got hot right away and the wooden spoon probably did not change temperature very much. If you cook marshmallows over a campfire, it's better to use a stick to hold the marshmallow than a metal clothes hanger because although you have to be careful not to let the stick catch on fire, it will not get too hot to handle.

Snow insulates plants. The cold of snow, which never gets colder than the freezing point of water or 32°F (0°C), doesn't hurt the plants as much as the cold air, which might be colder.

The highest temperature ever recorded in North America was at Furnace Creek Ranch in Death Valley, California. On July 10th, 1934 it was 134°F (56.7°C). Whew!

The Eighth Grade Revenge

Some of the seventh and eighth graders weren't too happy about losing to the younger kids. They were even more unhappy after Paloma posted photos of their winning sculpture on her blog and Einstein's mom had one published in the *Sparta Tribune*. There was a lot of grumbling and some angry looks in the cafeteria in the days after. Einstein did his best to ignore it, but some of his friends were getting annoyed, especially Paloma.

"We won fair and square," she complained, as they headed to lunch in the cafeteria two days later. "You even told them about using the blankets, so their sculptures wouldn't melt."

"They'll get over it," Einstein said, though he wasn't too sure.

"Next time, I'll side with Stanley," Paloma replied. "We won't help them at all." She stopped with her hand on the big swinging door to the cafeteria. "Hey, this door is stuck," she said, while pushing on it.

Just then Pat Hong came down the hallway. Without saying anything, he reached over Paloma's shoulder and put his hand on the door to push it open.

"Hey!" Paloma said, with a smile. "I can open doors for myself."

"Uh, I know," Pat stuttered, embarrassed, "I was just . . . I was . . . uh, go ahead."

As usual, Pat had trouble talking whenever Paloma was around. Everyone seemed to notice it except Paloma.

Paloma nodded, put her shoulder to the door and heaved. It moved slowly at first then swung open wide.

"There!" she said as she stepped aside to let Einstein and Pat enter. "That's a heavy door."

"Uh, yeah," Pat agreed. "It sure is heavy."

"It's the inertia," Einstein said, as they walked to an empty table.

"You're right," Paloma nodded as they sat down. Pat sat opposite her and looked intently into his brown paper lunch bag.

"Inertia," Einstein explained. "It's the tendency of objects to resist change in their state of motion. If an object is at rest it takes energy to get it to move."

Pat didn't look up from his sandwich. He just nodded and said, "You mean like the steel beams in the outer space play."

"That's right," Einstein said. "It's hard to get a door like that moving, but once it starts, it tends to keep going. Which brings up another important point."

"Yes?" Paloma said, with a pained expression.

"When is a door not a door?" Einstein asked with a giant grin.

"I know that," Paloma replied. "When it's ajar."

"Gee, did I tell you that one already?" Einstein asked. But Paloma didn't get to answer. Two eighth graders were standing at their table. One was a tall African American girl with long curly hair, who was wearing a jeans jacket over a green dress. The other was a very large blond boy, with a thick neck, wearing a black heavy metal T-shirt.

"Three o'clock," the boy almost grunted.

"Excuse me?" Paloma replied. Einstein knew she was trying to sound calm, but she looked worried. He saw Pat shift nervously in his seat.

"He said, three o'clock," the tall girl repeated. "We, the kids of the eighth grade, are challenging the sixth grade to a contest. Today. Three o'clock. In the schoolyard. Be there or all of Sparta will know you're cowards."

"Uh, what kind of competition?" Einstein asked, as he pushed his glasses up on his nose.

"You'll see," the boy growled.

"What do you mean?" Pat asked, sounding angry.

"Just be there—or else."

The two of them turned and left, swaggering

through the cafeteria. As they did, Stanley came running up to their table from the other direction.

"Did they tell you?" he asked, breathlessly.

"Yeah," Einstein replied. "We have a challenge."

"I know," Stanley nodded. "So if we all leave school early, we won't have to face them."

"Are you nuts?" Paloma cried. "We're not backing down. Right?"

"Right!" Pat nodded.

"Are you nuts?" Stanley said. "They're all bigger than us. They'll kill us."

"Stanley's right," Einstein said calmly. "We don't have to go."

"See?" Stanley said.

"But," Einstein continued. "I think we should go. I don't think they're going to fight us."

"Well, what do you think it is?" Paloma asked.

"I don't know," Einstein replied, trying to sound brave. "But whatever it is, we'll figure out a way to win."

The news spread quickly, through the hallways and by text message. At three o'clock practically the whole school was in the schoolyard waiting to see what would happen. Even Stanley showed up, though he stood as close to the gate as he could. There was still a lot of snow on the ground and everyone was dressed in their warm winter coats. Einstein, Paloma, Pat, and Jamal pushed through the crowd until they saw the two kids who had challenged them.

Einstein had learned the names of their challengers from other kids in school. He went up to the big blond kid and stuck out his hand.

"Hi, Gary. I'm Einstein Anderson," he said.

"Yeah, I know who you are, *Einstein*," Gary

replied with a sneer. "You're the kid who thinks he's such a genius."

"You're going to need more than brains to beat us this time," said the tall young woman, who came over followed by a group of other kids.

"Well, we're not afraid of you, Andrea," said Paloma.

"You better be afraid," Andrea replied. She towered over Paloma. "Because you are going to lose."

Einstein pushed his glasses back on his nose. "Excuse me," he asked very calmly. "But what exactly are we going to lose in?"

Andrea looked at Gary, who just shrugged. "We haven't figured that out yet," he said, not sounding quite as angry. "How about a tug of war?"

There were nods all around from the eighth graders.

"Anyone have a rope?" Gary asked the crowd.

"A tug of war isn't fair," Paloma said. "Most of you are bigger than we are."

"Oh, are you going to start crying?" Andrea sneered.

"Who's crying?" Paloma shot back.

"Excuse me," Einstein asked, still calm. "Since your side issued the challenge, it's only fair that we get to pick the contest."

Andrea shook her head, but Gary nodded. "Yeah, that's the way they do it in the movies," he explained to his friends. "But we want a real challenge," he said to Einstein. "No science quizzes."

"How about a race?" Einstein replied.

Gary's eyes widened with pleasure. "What kind of race?" he asked.

"A sled race," Einstein replied. "Across the pond in Brookdale Park. It's frozen over and kids are skating there." The park was just a block away.

"A sled race on the pond?" Andrea asked, sounding suspicious. "What's the catch."

"No catch," Einstein replied. "We get two sleds that are exactly the same. You pick two kids to sit on the sled and two kids to push. We do the same. We'll even start ten yards behind you, but you can't start until we get up to you. That way, we'll have to cover more ground than you do."

"You'll go further than us?" Gary asked.

"That's right," Einstein nodded. "Is it a deal?"

"Hold on!" someone shouted. It was Stanley. He'd forgotten to be scared and was pushing his way into the crowd. "Einstein is going to make the sixth grade lose!" he said. "Don't let him make that deal."

Gary grabbed Einstein's hand and shook it. "Too late!" he cried. "It's a deal. Now get ready to get beat!"

"Einstein, are you sure?" Pat Hong whispered to him. "I think you just made sure we're going to lose."

"Don't worry," Einstein whispered back. "I know we can beat them this way."

Can you solve the mystery? How can the sixth graders win if they start ten yards behind the eighth graders?

Most of the sixth grade and most of the eighth grade marched the block over to Brookdale Park. Meanwhile some kids who lived nearby ran home to get sleds. The pond was frozen solid, and luckily there was no one on it. Einstein and Gary chose two sleds that looked identical, then each grade picked their teams.

Einstein selected the two lightest kids in the sixth grade to sit on the sled and he chose Pat Hong and Harry Jackson to push. They lined up on the ice, with the sixth grade sled ten yards behind the eighth grade sled. It was about 40 yards across the pond.

"Someone yell start," Andrea called out. She was one of the pushers for the eighth grade team.

"I will!" Stanley volunteered. He stood to one side and in a loud voice, shouted, "Ready, set, go!"

The sixth grade team started pushing. They were pretty slow at first but by the time they got to the eighth grade sled they were flying. The eighth graders started up but it was no use, by the time they got up to speed, the sixth graders were halfway to the other side. They won easily and a big cheer went up from the younger kids.

"You cheated!" Gary shouted, looking down at Einstein.

"No, we both agreed to the rules," Einstein told him.

"Then how did you beat us?" Gary demanded.

"Well, it has to do with the scientific principle of …" Einstein began, but just then, Paloma ran over and interrupted him.

"It was just luck," Paloma said quickly. "A freak accident. There's no way us little sixth graders should have won. Come on Einstein, don't we have to be somewhere?"

Paloma pushed and dragged Einstein away from Gary who was left fuming on the ice.

"But it wasn't luck," Einstein protested, as he, Paloma, Pat, and the other sixth graders walked out of the park.

"I know," Paloma told him. "It was inertia. But you don't have to tell *them* that. It will just get them angrier."

"Inertia, again?" Pat asked.

"Sure," Einstein replied. "A sled loaded down with two kids has a lot of inertia when it's at rest. You need a lot of force to get it moving. But once the sled is moving, inertia helps keep it going. It's a lot easier to push once you get your speed up."

"But both sleds were the same," Pat asked Einstein. "Didn't they have the same amount of inertia?"

"That's what I was going to say," Stanley added.

"Sure, Stanley," Paloma muttered.

"Yes, but you started pushing earlier," said Einstein. "By the time the eighth graders started to push, you were going at full speed. You were yards ahead by the time they got going. In a short race like this, they had no chance to catch up."

"Einstein," Pat laughed. "I'm sure glad your brain is on *our* side."

"Hey," Einstein said, "that reminds me."

Everyone started to groan, but Pat spoke up. "Let Einstein tell his joke," he said. "He earned it."

Einstein was already laughing. "Do you know

why the fish could operate on brains? Because it was a brain sturgeon!"

From: Einstein Anderson
To: Science Geeks
Experiment: Marvelous Magic to Amaze and Mystify

These tricks take a little practice, but once you get the hang of it, you can use the laws of inertia to amaze your friends. Let's give it a try!

Here is what you need:

• A plastic cup or drinking glass

• A playing card or piece of cardboard big enough to cover the top of the cup

• A marble

• A piece of cloth with no hem

• A plastic plate

• Silverware

• An aluminum pie plate

• A paper towel roll

• A baseball

Put the plastic cup on a table and put the playing card over the top. Then put the marble in the middle of the playing card. Wait a moment until everything is still and then flick the card with your finger, hard enough to knock it off the cup. What happens?

Now try a more advanced version. Put the cloth on the table, with one edge hanging over the side. (Be sure it is just a flat piece of cloth with no hem. A hem will

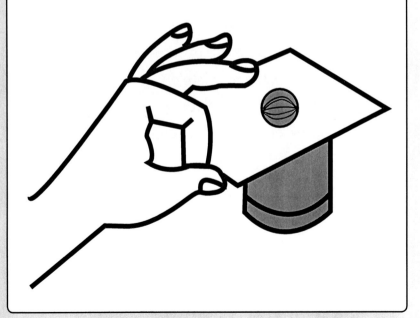

catch the dishes and ruin the magic.) Arrange the plastic plates and plastic dishes on top. You can even put some water in the plastic drinking glass (you might want to try this outside or in a kitchen where you can easily clean up a spill until you get the hang of it). With a grand flourish, pull DOWN sharply and quickly on the edge of the cloth that's hanging over the side of the table. The dishes should stay on top, while the tablecloth pulls out from under them.

Finally, you can build to a dramatic conclusion: put the drinking glass with water in it on the bottom, put the pie plate on top and then balance a baseball (hardball works best) on top of the paper towel roller. With a smooth hit, knock the pie plate off the top of the glass. The paper tube will go with it, but the baseball should fall into the water glass with a splash. Bravo!

What's going on here?

The Science Solution

Way back in 1687, Sir Isaac Newton published a book called *Philosophiæ Naturalis Principia*, or "Principles of Natural Philosophy." Isaac was an English scientist and a very great observer of the world around him. He also lived at a time called the "scientific revolution" when many scientists were working on understanding, scientifically, how our universe works. They all talked and debated and shared their ideas. In his book Newton described three laws of motion that still serve as the basis for our understanding of physics. Even more amazing, Newton's laws of motion apply not only on Earth, but also in outer space! Newton's first law is the law of *inertia*. It says that an object at rest stays at rest until some force causes it to move. By the same law, an object that is moving will stay in motion until some force causes it to stop. Inertia is the basis for all the magic tricks we just performed.

In the first example with the playing card and the marble, everything would have stayed as it was, but you exerted force on the playing card when you flicked it with your finger. Inertia made the marble stay in place, but when the card was gone, the force of gravity caused the marble to fall into the cup. The second example, with the tablecloth, works the same way. Because of inertia, the objects on top of the cloth don't move. In the third example with the paper tube and the baseball, the force you exerted on the pie plate was transferred to the tube when the edge of the pie plate hit it, so the tube also fell out of the way. But good old inertia kept the ball where it was, until gravity pulled it down into the glass of water.

I don't know about you, but inertia keeps me in bed on Saturday morning until the force of my brother Dennis gets me up!

CPSIA information can be obtained at www.ICGtesting.com
Printed in the USA
BVOW03s0206270813

329590BV00008B/197/P